A

REFERENCE ONLY

A glossary of mining terms

1850220530

CORNWALL COUNTY COUNCIL
LIBRARIES AND ARTS DEPARTMENT

A GLOSSARY
of
MINING TERMS

Edited by

W. G. ORCHARD

DYLLANSOW
TRURAN

First published 1990 by Dyllansow Truran, 'Trewolsta', Trewirgie, Redruth, Kernow.

© 1991 W. G. Orchard

ISBN No. 185022 053 0

Typeset by St. George Typesetting, Commercial Centre, Pool Industrial Estate, Redruth, Cornwall TR15 3QT. Tel: (0209) 217033.

Printed and bound by Short Run Press Ltd., Exeter.

FOREWORD

A considerable time has elapsed since a glossary of mining terms has been published. J. Y. Watson's "Compendium of British Mining" and "The Prospector's Handbook" by J. W. Anderson, published in 1843 and 1911 respectively, both contained a short glossary within their covers.

Many new books on Cornish Mining and its history have been written in the last twenty years or so. This publication containing terms relevant to old and modern mining practice seems to fill a need in this respect.

L. J. Bullen
Chairman – Cornish Mining Development Association

PREFACE

It is said that up to the 19th century
it was the habit of old miners to place a little
image of clay over the first set of timbers on
the entrance to a level, and that when the level was begun a
curious formula was uttered beginning
   "Send for the merry curse and the priest"
The late Mr Morton Nance, wrote that this represented
the beginning of a prayer addressed to Camborne's
patron Saint in Cornish.
   "Sen-Meryasek-ny-a-th-Pys"
i.e. Saint Meryasek, we pray thee.

I have tried through the contents of this little book (published by
Dyllansow Truran) to compile a glossary of mining terms as used in
mining districts throughout Cornwall.

There are some mineralogical, and geological terms which would not
have been in the miners' common parlance, there are terms which are
now purely archaic, and there are those terms which continue in use.

There are times in the leisured moments of interested people when their
attention is attracted by the early romance of Cornish mining, and the
craftsmanship of the miners, and a pleasant hour is spent in reading
of these workers of a past age. Their development resulted in many
influences on local and overseas tradition, so that it can be said that,
the counties industrial history is written in them.

The compilation of this volume has involved the willing help of others
and it would be ungracious not to acknowledge, with grateful thanks,
the ready assistance given. To the following I would like to give a special
thanks, to Mr. Joffre Bullen, for his reading, checking, and providing
photographs, also the late Mr. Percy W. Bonds, for supplying me with so
many of the terms used, and to Dr. Victor Phillips of C.S.M. who first
put me in touch with Mr. Bonds, when I started to compile this glossary
in 1986.

W. G. Orchard. 1989

(A)

Acicular
    Slender, straight, crystals.

Adit-level
    A horizontal drift or tunnel, through which the water pumped or drawn thereto by the engine from the bottom of the mine and the water descending from above by percolation, passes off by gravitation.

    This level is usually commenced at the bottom of the deepest neighbouring valley, and extended through the whole, or greatest part of the mine.

    It is often, (always when convenient) driven on a lode, which it proves in its progress or on a flookan or cross course, when more convenient, because it's less expensive than when driven through the "country".

    There are deep and shallow adits.

    The County adit, including its branches is 38 miles long. Its greatest depth is 70 fathoms. (See Fig 5).

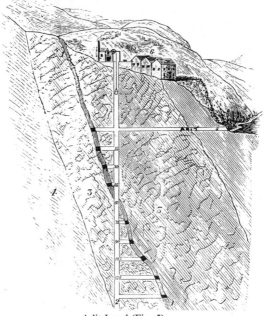

Adit Level (Fig. 5)

1

Acid

Radical of any salt.

Adventurers

Those who have shares in a mine, similar to but not quite the same as modern shareholders.

Aggregated

When the component parts of a body only adhere together and may be separated by mechanical means; but less intimately mixed than in a compound.

Air-Machine

An apparatus for forcing fresh air into, or withdrawing foul air from, badly ventilated places.

Air-Pipes

Tubes or pipes made of iron or wood used for ventilating underground by conveying atmospheric air into levels having but one communication with the surface, and thus no current of air.

Air-Shaft

A shaft sunk for ventilation.

Aitch-Piece

That part of a plunger lift in which the clacks are fixed.

Alliaceous

The garlic odour of arsenical minerals when heated or struck.

Amorphous

Of irregular shape; without crystalline form.

Anhydrous

Without water or crystallization.

Arborescent

Ramifying like a tree.

Arch

A piece of ground left unworked near a shaft, or in a level, to keep open the ground.

Arched-Levels

Rare in Cornish mines.

Argillaceous

Consisting of clay.

Arsenic

Soot collected in burning flues, oxide cleaned from the calcination of arsenic sulphide.

Arseniate

The arsenic acid united with a base, as copper in the arseniate of

2

copper.

Assay-House

    The house in which the ores are assayed.

Attle

    Rubbish containing little or no ore; debris, deads.

Average produce

    The quantity of fine copper contained in 100 parts of ore, having a produce of $10\frac{5}{8}$, contains $10\frac{5}{8}\%$ of copper, being above average of copper ores in Cornwall.

Average-standard

    The price per ton of fine copper in the ore, after adding returning charges for smelting of £2:15:0 (£2.75) per ton of ore in Cornwall, or £2:5:0 (£2.25) per ton of ore in Swansea. The regulation of the standard depends entirely on the price which fine copper bears in the market, rising and falling in the same proportion. Supposing the produce of a parcel of ore to be 10, and the price at which it was sold to the smelter to be £8:18:0, the standard of that parcel will be thus obtained; 10 tons of the ore will be required to yield 1 ton of fine copper; therefore, £8:18:0 x 10 = £89 will be the value of the ore containing a ton of metal. For the same reason, the returning charge of £2:15:0, must be multiplied by 10 making £27:10:0, which added to the former sum of £89, makes £116:10:0, being the average of that parcel. Low produce ore will naturally have a higher standard.

(B)

Back

    The back of a lode is the part nearest the surface. The back of a level is the lode or ground standing above it.

Bal

    The miners' term for a mine; a very old term.

Balance bob

    A counterpoise of the line of rods in engine shaft. (See Fig 7).

Bar of ground

    A vein or rock of a different description from that in its vicinity.

Bargain

    A miner's contract to do certain work at a certain price.

Barrow

    (see wheel barrow & hand barrow).

3

Engine here.

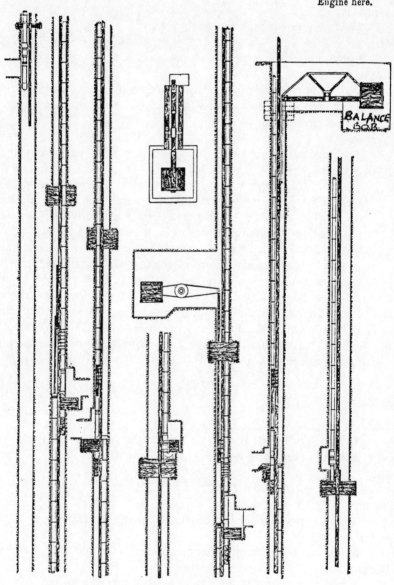

Cornish Pit Work (Fig. 7)

4

Batch of ore
> A certain quantity of ore sent to the surface by any pare of men. (Pare meaning party).

Bearers
> Supports to the pumps in the engine shaft.

Beat away
> To excavate; usually applied to hard ground.

Bed
> A seam, or horizontal vein of ore.

Bend
> Indurated clay; a name given by miners to any indurated argillaceous substance.

Bit
> The steeled end of a borer.

Black Jack
> Blende (zinc).

Black Tin
> Tin ore ready for smelting. (Tin Oxide).

Blast
> The air introduced into a furnace.

Blast Holes
> The holes through which the water enters the windbore, or bottom of a pump.

Blasting
> Forcing of portions of rock by means of gunpowder, or other explosive. A hole is made with a borer, into which the explosive is inserted, then confined, and ignited; hence the blast.

Blende
> One of the ores of zinc, composed of iron, zinc, sulphur, silex, and water; on being scratched it emits a phosphoric light.

Block Tin
> Metallic tin.

Blower
> A smelter.

Bob
> The engine beam, or lever, transmitting the power from the engine to the pit-work. (Fig 1 & 2).

Bob-pit
> The pit in which the balance bob works. (Fig 7).

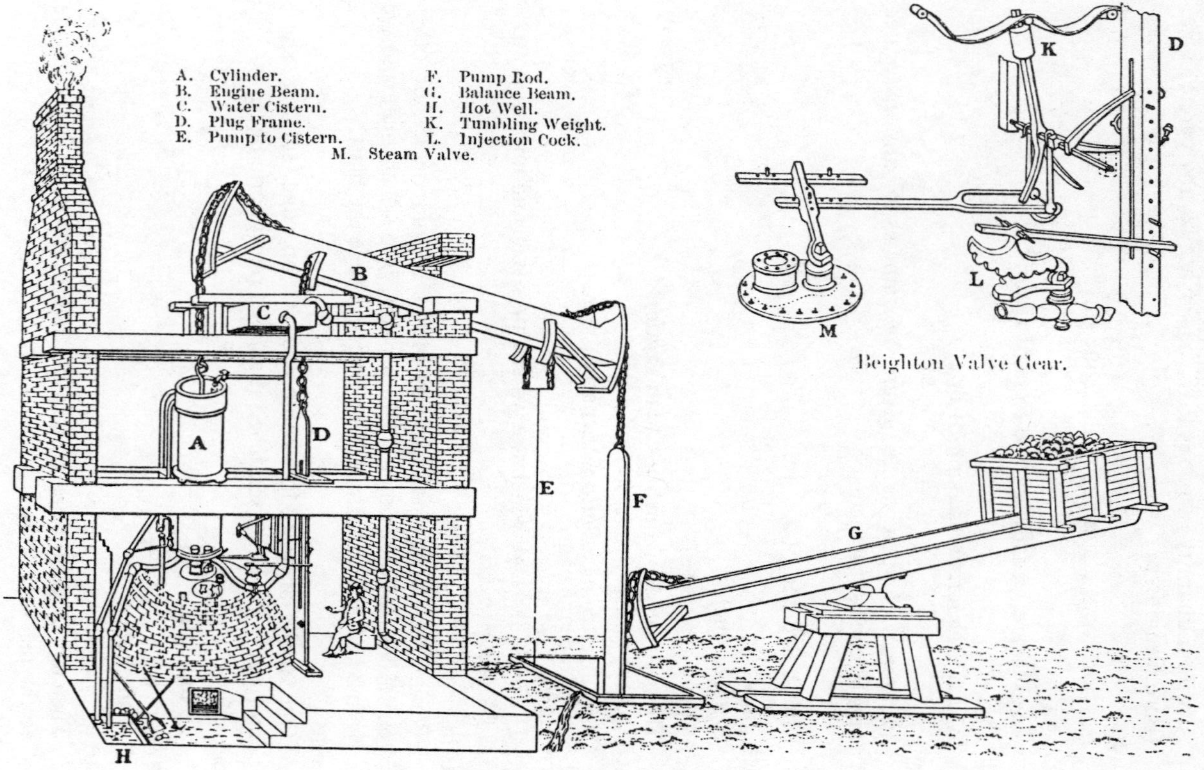

Beighton Valve Gear.

A. Cylinder.
B. Engine Beam.
C. Water Cistern.
D. Plug Frame.
E. Pump to Cistern.
F. Pump Rod.
G. Balance Beam.
H. Hot Well.
K. Tumbling Weight.
L. Injection Cock.
M. Steam Valve.

(Fig. 1) Newcomen Steam Fire Engine

6

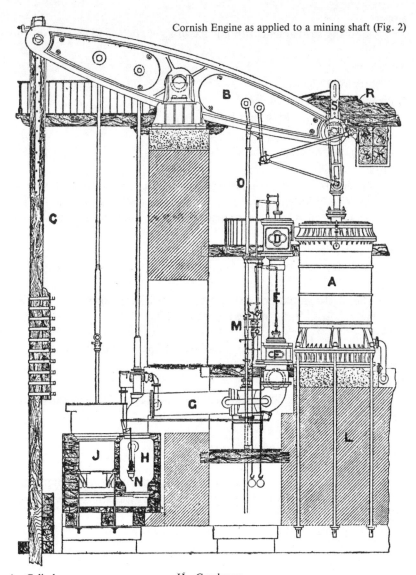

Cornish Engine as applied to a mining shaft (Fig. 2)

A = Cylinder	H = Condenser
B = Beam	J = Air pump
C = Pump Rod	L = Loading of masonry to take holding down bolts
D = Steam and equilibrium valve box	M = Valve gear
E = Equilibrium pipe	N = Injection valve
F = Exhaust valve box	R = Spring beams (wooden)
G = Exhaust pipe to the condenser	S = Catch pieces of engine beam

Borer

A boring instrument with a piece of steel at the end called a boring bit.

Boring machine

(See rock drill).

Bottoms

The lowest workings either in a stope, level, or elsewhere.

Boulders

Large stones, or pebbles.

Bounds

The limits of a given area for mining. Anciently set out by order of the Vice-Warden of the Stannaries when the land owners of waste lands declined to grant license for mining therein. This power still exists.

Bonney

A distinct bed of ore that communicates with no mineral vein.

Brace

The platform placed over the mouth of a shaft, or winze, to which the tackle is fixed; at the top of a shaft.

Brake

A friction band, or other contrivance to regulate the motion of a winch, etc.

Branch

A small vein which separates from the lode, and generally unites again therewith.

Brood

Impurities mixed with the ores.

Bryle, Bril, or Broil

The traces of the presence of a lode found in the loose matter, on or near the surface.

Bucket

The piston of the lifting pump. (Fig 5 & 4).

Bucket-Lift

A set of iron pipes attached to a lifting pump. (Fig 6).

Bucket rods

Wooden rods, to which the piston of a lifting pump is attached. (Fig 6 & 4).

Bucker

The person who reduces the ore by bucking.

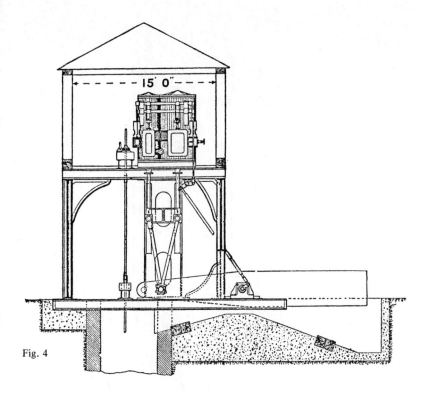

Fig. 4

Bucking
    The reduction of the ore for the separation of waste.
Bucking iron
    The iron or tool with which the copper ore is pulverized.
Bucking plate
    An iron plate on which the ore is placed for being bucked.
Buddle
    An apparatus by which the stamped tin is washed from its impurities. There were various contrivances in use eg. Brunton's frame, the Round buddle, (Borlase's) Zenner's Rotating Buddle. (Fig 12).
Buddling
    Separating the ores from the earthy substance, by means of an inclined hutch or cistern.
Bunch, or squat of ore
    A quantity of ore of small extent; more than a stone, and not so much as a course.

9

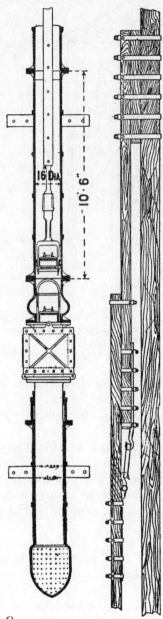

Pit Work Bucket Lift (Fig. 6)

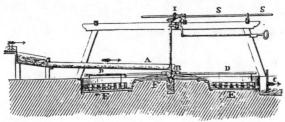

Buddling (Fig. 12)

The finely-powdered ore, passing from the stamp grates is treated in a variety of ways, in buddles, frames, kieves, etc., but the aim and end of all these operations is the same, the separation of the heavy ore from the lighter waste by the action of gravity, the difference of gravity being aided by partially suspending the ore in water.

To describe one of the processes, that of "buddling". fig 12, is a section of the ordinary convex buddle. E E is a circular pit about 18 or 20 feet in diameter, and 2 feet 6 inches deep at the sides. F, is a raised table, 5 or 6 feet in diameter, highest in the centre, and sloping outwards in all directions; the floor of the pit, E E, also slopes outwards as shown. The stamped ore suspended in water, forming a very thin mud, passes in the direction of the arrows into the hopper at H, and is strained through a grating which keeps back any chips of wood or coarse waste which may have got into the channel. The ore passes down the channel, A, in the direction of the arrow, and flows into the cup, B, of the central table, and from here is distributed by six or eight openings or channels over the central table, and thence over the floor, E, of the buddle. D D are brushes, four or six in number, which revolve and spread the ore evenly over the floor of the buddle. The whole is moved by the bevel wheels I, by means of shafting, S S, communicating motion from a water wheel, or other source of power.

Bunney

    (See Bonney)

Burden, or overburn

    The substances reposing on a bed of stream tin ore; also those over china clay; or quarry stone.

Burning-House

    The furnace in which tin ores are calcined to sublime the sulphur from pyrites; the latter being thus decomposed are more readily removed by washing.

Burrow

    A heap of deads, attle, rubbish.

(C)

Cage of a Whim

    The barrel on which the rope is wound up.

Cab

    A poor part of a lode.

Cairn or carn
　A heap of stones on an eminence.

Cal
　Wolfram

Calamine
　An ore of zinc

Calciner
　An apparatus for roasting ore. (To remove arsenic).

Call
　A demand on the adventurers to pay their share of costs.

Cann, or Kand
　Fluor Spar, largely produced, formerly, in Wheal Gorland, Gwennap.

Capel
　A stone composed of quartz, (schorl) and hornblende, usually occurring on one or both walls of a lode, and more frequently accompanying tin than copper ores.

Cap'n
　(see Captain).

Capstan
　A machine consisting of an axle and several long arms, by which pumps and other materials are let down, or raised from, shafts by manual force; there were also steam capstans for like use.

Capsule
　A fulminate enclosed in a short copper tube for firing a charge of dynamite.

Captains or mine agents
　Men who superintend the operations at and in the mine. There are surface captains, who attend exclusively to surface work, and captain dressers, whose duties are limited to the milling department, the head captain is called the manager; but where a committee exists his powers are small.

Carbona
　A large mass of ore, not a lode or lodes. The most remarkable known were those at St. Ives Consols.

Carrack
　(See capel).

Cast-after-cast
　The throwing up of tinstuff, from one stage of boards to another, the stages being 6 feet apart.

Cases of spar

Veins of quartz (not containing ores) which have not a position or direction parallel to the lodes.

Casing

A division of wooden planks, separating a footway, or a whim or engine shaft, from one another; or the boarding round a shaft, for its security.

Catch-pit

Where slimes are retained for dressing.

Cataract

An arrangement to regulate the stroke of a Cornish draught engine.

Cathead

A small capstan.

Caunter, or contra lode

A lode which diverges at a considerable angle from the direction of the other lodes in its vicinity.

Charger

An implement in the form of the bit of a carpenter's augur, used for charging holes for blasting, which are dug horizontally.

Chain

A modern substitute for the hemp rope for drawing up the ores, etc. from the mine by the whim, now entirely superseded by the wire rope. (First used 1830).

Chats

Small heaps of ore.

Chimming

A process of similar effect to tossing, but being performed on small quantities of ore, the kieve is supported on the verge of its bottom.

Cistern

A spacious box at the bottom of each lift in the engine shaft.

Chlorite

Peach.

Clack

The valve of a pump of any description.

Clack door

The aperture through which the clack of a pump is fixed and removed.

Clapper

A contrivance at the top of a shaft to sound from the mine to the engine man.

Clay slate

Argillaceous rock (killas).

Claying

Lining the hole (in which an explosive is placed) with clay, to prevent the explosive from becoming damp.

Cleavage

Lamination.

Cob

To break the ores with hammers in such a manner as to enable persons to separate the dead or worthless part by picking.

Cobber

A person who cobs.

Cockle

Schorl.

Cofer

A case containing a set of stampers or lifters from 3 to 6 in number.

Cofering

Securing the shaft from the influx of water by ramming the clay in.

Coffin

Old workings open to the surface, mostly made by the ancient workers, called "old men".

Collar of a shaft

The timber by which its upper parts are kept from caving in.

Collar launder

The pipe or gutter at the top of a lift of pumps through which the water is conveyed to the cistern.

Comby lode

Many alternating layers of quartz and other minerals.

Connection or connecting rods

The pumping rods in the shaft which are attached to the engine beam. (Fig 2).

Core

Miners usually work but 6 hours at a time, and consequently four pares of men are required for the whole time - forenoon core, from 6am to noon; afternoon core from noon to 6pm; first core by night from 6pm to midnight; and last core by night from midnight to 6 am; 8hr cores have come into vogue.

Cost book

Cornish mines were formerly all conducted on the unlimited principle. Some of them were on the 'Limited' principle but these were usually of temporary existence.

The method is to enter in the "cost book" the name and address of each of the adventurers who commence working the mine, all subsequent transfers of shares, and every expense attached to the undertaking. A meeting is held every 2 months, when the purser presents his accounts, made up for that period. Consequently the shareholders are enabled to judge the profitable or unprofitable nature of the undertaking before any extensive liabilities are incurred; and any one feeling dissatisfied may, on paying his proportion of the debts due, sign his name off the "cost book", as it is termed and by which action he ceases to be liable for any future costs. The "cost book" rules were often violated in several ways.

Costeaning

Sinking pits transversely in a line with the lode to discover its position; commonly called "Prospecting".

Country

The stratum of rock through which the lode passes.

Course-of-ore

A portion of the lode containing a regular vein of ore.

Cover

The box into which the ore is removed from the rock; also the place at the head of the trunk, in which the slimes are agitated, mechanically suspended in water, in the process of trunking.

Crease

Divisions of buddled work.

Crib or curb

A circular frame of wood, screwed together as a foundation for bucking or pulverizing ore in the shaft.

Crop

The best ore.

Cross course

A lode or vein (It is really a fault where one side has moved relative to the other generally non metallic) which intersects a metallic lode and throws it out of its regular course, in some cases (but rarely) as much as 80 fathoms. This effect is called a "heave" or "throw".

Cross cut

A level driven at right angles to the direction or strike of the lode.

Crushing

Grinding of the ores.

Crusher

A machine for reducing the ores, sometimes worked by steam and sometimes by water power.

Cube

A solid figure, contained under 6 equal squares.

Cuneiform

Wedge-shaped.

Cupelo

A small furnace.

Cut

To intersect by driving, sinking, or rising.

Cut-out

When a course of ore terminates suddenly.

Cylinder

The circular case of iron in which the piston receives the steam to give the motion to the engine. (Fig 3 Steam), (Fig 9 Water Bailing).

(D)

Dam

A barrier constructed to shut out or to impound water, also a choke damp; foul air.

Deads

Attle or mine rubbish, useless stuff.

Dead Ground

A portion of the lode in which there is no ore.

Dean

The end of a level or cross cut, fore-breast.

Deep adit

The deepest adit in the mine.

Diallage

A mincral of a lamellar or foliated structure occurring largely in the Lizard peninsular, containing magnesia.

Dialler

The person who makes the underground survey.

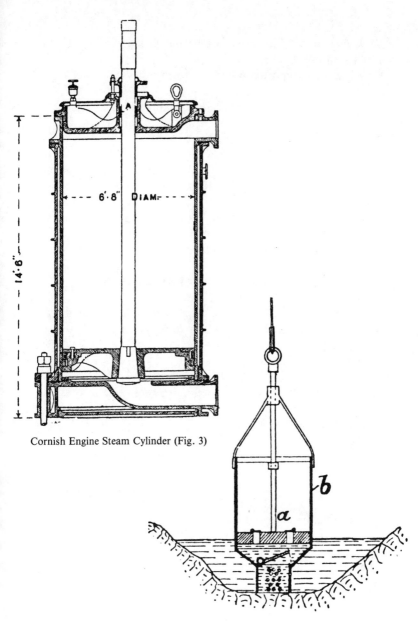

Cornish Engine Steam Cylinder (Fig. 3)

Bailing Tank Cylinder For Water (Fig. 9)
A = Piston   B = Cylinder

Dialling
  Surveying for the purpose of preparing a plan.
Dileuing (Terluing)
  Washing ore, supported on a hair-bottom sieve in water.
Dip-of-lode
  Its underlie. Angle between the horizontal and the lode.
Dippa
  A small pit.
Dish
  That portion of the produce of a mine which is paid to the mineral owner, also called royalty, or dues.
Dissuing
  Is when the lode is small and rich, to break down the stratum from one of its walls, by which means it can afterwards be taken away without being deteriorated, and without waste.
Divisional planes
  Partitions in the rock having a northerly direction.
Dowsing rod
  The Hazel rod, by which some persons are said to have discovered lodes by attraction called also "Divining".
Draught-engine
  An engine used for pumping.
Dredging ore
  A stone impregnated or traversed by minute veins of ore.
Dressers
  Cleaners of the ore.
Dressing floors
  The place where the ore is separated from its matrix.
Drift
  The excavation made for a roadway underground, a level.
Drill
  A machine invented for boring blasting holes expeditiously by steam power. (Later compressed air).
Driving
  Digging horizontally.
Dropper
  A branch when it leaves the main lode.
Druse
  Cavity in a vein, same as vugh.

18

Dry

A place fitted with steam pipes and other heating apparatus, where in miners underground cloths are dried.

Dues

The proportion of the returns paid to the owner of the land or minerals.

Dynamite

An explosive used in blasting. Introduced in 1860.

Durns

A frame of timber with boards placed behind it to keep open the ground in shafts, levels, etc.

Dzhu, or Hulk

To dig away a portion of the rock etc, on one side of the end that the blast may be more efficient.

(E)

Elvan

Porphyry, clay, stone.

End

The further extent of a level or cross-cut, the "Fore-Breast".

Engine

A machine of any construction to effect the drainage of the mine, to haul the stuff, to reduce the same, and for winding and other purposes; generally worked by steam; in some places by water. (Figs 1 & 2).

Engineer

The superintendent of machinery.

Engine man

Man who attends to, & works the machine.

Engine pool

A pond for supplying the engine with condensing water.

Engine shaft

The pit or shaft through which the water is drawn by the engine from the mine to the adit or surface or both. (See Fig 1F).

(F)

Fang

A niche cut out in the side of an adit, or shaft, to serve as an air course; sometimes a main of wooden pipes is denominated by "fanging". Miners also apply it to their wages by saying that they have "fanged" so much in a month.

Farm

That part of a lord's fee which is taken for liberty to work in tin mines only that are bounded; generally one fifteenth.

Fast

The firm rock beneath the deluvium, shelf.

Feeder

A branch when it falls into the lode.

Feldspar

One of the constituents of granite.

Fire whim

(See steam whim).

Flang

A two pointed pick.

Flat rods

Rods for communicating motion from the engine horizontally to another part of the mine called the "flat-rod shaft".

Flat rope

A whim rope introduced about 1834.

Floran Tin

Tin ore scarcely perceptible in the stone; tin ore stamped very small.

Flookan

A soft clayey substance, which is generally found to accompany the cross-courses and sides, and occasionally the lodes themselves; but when applied to a vein, it means a cross vein or course composed of clay, some of which are several fathoms in width.

Floors

(See Dressing Floors).

Flues

The connection between a boiler and chimney also chambers in which the arsenic soot is collected.

Fluke

The head of the charger; an instrument used for cleaning the hole previous to blasting.

Fluor spar

Fluoride of calcium, used as a flux by copper-ore smelters. In the 1830's it was raised plentifully at Wheal Gorland, in Gwennap.

Footwall
> The wall under the lode; also sometimes called the underlying wall.

Footway
> The ladders by which the workmen descend and ascend in the mine it is also the name of the shaft in which the ladders are fixed.

Forcepiece
> A piece of timber placed in a level or shaft etc, in a diagonal position to keep the ground open.

Fore-breast
> The front end of a drift.

Fork
> Water in fork, water all drawn out; the bottom of the engine shaft. (The saying to fork out).

Frame
> An apparatus for cleaning the tin contained in slime, by action of water. There are hand frames, and automatic frames. i.e. frames worked without manpower but by water-wheels. (Dolcoath had more than a hundred of these).

Fuggan
> Pastry containing meat on the top, taken by miners for a lunch. (See Hoggan).

(G)

Gad
> A pointed wedge of a peculiar form, having sides of a parabolic figure.

Galena
> Sulphide of lead.

Gallery
> A level or tunnel in the mine.

Glist (Schist)
> Mica.

Good level
> Levels driven nearly horizontally, and of fair dimensions.

Gossan
> Peroxide of iron and quartz, generally occurring on the backs of lodes.

Granite
> Igneous rock, composed of quartz, feldspar, and mica.

Grass
    The surface of the mine.
Grain tin
    Crystalline tin ore; metallic tin smelted with charcoal.
Grate
    Stamps grate, a metal plate pierced with small holes; it is fixed to
    the stamps frame, and through the holes the stamped ore passes.
Greenstone
    Traprock (volcanic rock) contains hornblende and feldspar in
    small crystals.
Greisen
    An altered granitic rock.
Griddle, or Riddle
    A sieve.
Grinder
    A machine for crushing ores between iron cylinders or barrels.
    Otherwise known as rolls.
Ground
    The country; the stratum in which the lode is found.
Growan
    Decomposed granite; but sometimes applied to the solid rock.
Guag
    A place that has been wrought before for tin.
Gulph of ore
    A very large deposit of ore in a lode.
Gunnies
    A level or working.
Gurt
    A gutter; a channel for water.

(H)

Hade
    The underlie of veins.
Halvans
    The ores that are not rich enough for sale until more of the
    impurities with which they are mixed have been removed, by
    water operations.
Halvanner
    The dresser or operator of the halvans.

Hand-barrow

A frame or box for conveying stone carried between two men.

Hanging wall

The upper wall of a lode.

Hauling

Drawing ore or attle out of the mine.

Head sword

The water running through the adit.

Head tin

A preparation of tin ore towards the working of it into metal.

Heave

The horizontal dislocation which occurs when one lode is intersected by a crosscourse. A right or left hand heave is, when the part of the intersected lode on the opposite side of the traversing vein is found by turning either to the right or left.

Haematite

The name of two ores of iron; the red haematite and the brown haematite.

Hoggan

The miner's lunch, consisting of baked pastry containing figs or currants, made convenient for the pocket.

Holing

When two drifts or levels meet.

Hook handles

The handles by which a windlass is worked.

Hornblende Schist

A slatey variety of hornblende, generally including feldspar and grains of quartz.

Hornstone

Schistoid flinty rock.

Horse

The dead ground included between two branches of a lode, at the point of their separation.

Horse-Whim

A machine, worked by a horse or horses for drawing up ores etc.

House of Water

A vugh or space, whether artificially excavated or not, filled with water.

Horse Arm
> The part of the horse whim to which the horses are attached to apply leverage for winding the kibble.

H piece
> See aitch piece.

Huel
> See Wheal.

Hutch
> Cistern or box.

Hydrons
> A mineral when it contains water of crystallization.

(I)

Idle
> When a mine is abandoned, or work has stopped.

Intersection
> Where one vein crosses another, and where a drift strikes a lode.

Ironstone
> Hard clay slate, hornblende, Hornblende slate, hornstone.

(J)

Jigger
> Cleaner of ores.

Jigging
> Separating the ore with a griddle or wire bottom sieve, the heavier substance passing through the bottom or lower part of the sieve; the lighter substances remaining on the upper part are put by for halvans.

Joints
> Short irregular partings in the rock.

Junction
> The meeting of strata, lodes, etc.

Jumper
> A long borer, worked by one person in a quarry.

(K)

Keenly
> See kindly.

Kieve
> A large circular vat.

Kibble
    A bucket usually made of iron, in which the ore, etc., is drawn to
    the surface. See Fig 8.
Kibble Filler
    The man who sends up the ore, etc., to the surface.
Killas
    Clay slate.
Kindly, or Keenly
    Apparently favourable ground for ore.

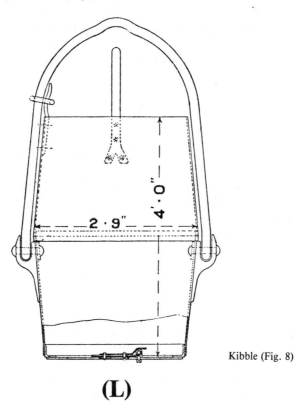

Kibble (Fig. 8)

(L)

Laminated
    Consisting of plates, scales, or layers, one over the other.
Lander
    The man who attends at the mouth of the shaft to receive the
    kibble, skip or cage in which the ore, or rubbish is drawn to the
    surface, to discharge it.

25

Lappior
    The dresser of the leavings.
Laths
    The boards that are put behind and supported by the "durns".
Launders
    Tubes or gutters for the conveyance of water; their form being
    that of a long box, having no cover or ends.
Lead Spar
    Sulphate of lead.
Leader of the lode
    A branch or small vein; part of the main lode.
Learies
    Empty places; old workings or vughs.
Lease
    The deed from the lord authorizing the works.
Leat
    A water course.
Leavings
    The ores which are left after the "crop" is taken out.
Levels
    Galleries driven on the lode usually at 10, 20, 30 fathoms etc.,
    below the adit.
License
    See tacknote.
Limited Companies
    Members of mining or other companies formed under the limited
    liability Acts are not liable beyond the amount of shares which
    they engage to take in the mine etc.
Limp
    A scraper to collect the skimpings in copper ore dressing.
Lift
    A series of pumps, bolted together for the conduct of water up the
    shaft as pumped by the engine; usually 10 to 40 fathoms in length.
    In a deep mine the lifts are very numerous. Figs 6 & 7.
Lifters
    Wooden beams, or thick iron rods to which the iron stamp heads
    are attached and lifted by the stamping engine for reducing the
    tinstone.
Lobby
    An open drain.

Lock-piece
A piece of timber used in supporting the workings.
Lode
A regular vein producing or affording any kind of metallic ores.
Lode Stovvan
A drang driven towards rising ground on the indications of a lode in marshy ground.
Lode Stuff
The undressed mineral from lodes.
Loobs
Slime containing ore.
Lost levels
Levels which are not driven horizontally.

(M)

Machine Whim
A rotary steam engine employed for winding.
Main Rod
The rod connecting the engine beam with forcing pumps in shaft. (Fig 1F and 2C).
Mallet
An instrument used in striking the borer.
Man-Engine
An engine used for letting down, and lifting up men from underground; first used about 1830 at Tresavean mine.
Manager
The agent having the control of the operations at the mine; "The General Manager".
Material Man
One who delivers out, and has care of the materials, candles, explosives, picks, etc, in the material house.
Meat Earth
The vegetable mould.
Mica Schist
Schistose rock abounding in mica.
Mock Lead
Blende.
More
A large quantity of ore in a particular part of the lode is called a "more" of tin.

Moorstone
    Granite. Found on surface and not quarried.
Mundic
    Iron pyrites.
Mun-Any
    Fusible metal.

(N)

Needle or Nail
    A long taper piece of copper, or iron with a copper point, used
    when tamping the hole for blasting, to make, by its withdrawal, an
    aperture for the insertion of the rush or train of powder.
Nogs, or Nays
    Support for the roof of a mine.

(O)

Ochre
    Clayey oxide of iron.
Old Men's Workings
    Any ancient underground workings. Excavations near the surface
    on the lode. Most of the lodes known in Cornwall and Devon were
    discovered by the ancient miners, who worked principally on the
    "backs".
Outcrop
    The lode appearing at surface.

(P)

Pack
    To occasion the speedy subsidence or settlement of the ore in the
    process of tossing or chimming, by beating the kieve in which it is
    contained with a hammer.
Parcel
    A heap of ore dressed and ready for sale.
Pare
    A gang or party of men.
Pass
    An opening left for letting down stuff to the level; also the slide by
    which tin-stone is let down to the stamps.

Pasty
> Potatoes and meat enclosed in pastry, easy to carry in the pocket for a lunch, or dinner.

Peach
> Chlorite.

Pedn Cairn
> A bunch of ore at a distance from the lode.

Pick
> A well known instrument of common use for breaking the ground, especially by miners.

Picker or poker
> A hand chisel for drilling which is held in one hand, and struck by the hammer with the other hand.

Pillar
> A piece of ground left to support the roof or hanging wall.

Pitch
> Limits of the piece of land set to tributers; to work on the lode at so much in the pound of the yield.

Pitch Bag
> A bag covered with pitch, into which powder is put that it may be protected from moisture, (before being put into a damp hole).

Pitman
> One employed to look after the lifts of pumps and drainage.

Pitwork
> The pumps and other apparatus of the engine shaft. Figs 6 & 7.

Plat
> An excavation or place to contain any ore or deads.

Plunger Pole
> The piston or forcer of a forcing pump.

Plunger Lift
> The set of pipes attached to a forcing pump.

Point of the Horse
> The spot where the vein is divided into two or more branches.

Polrose (pronounced Pulrose)
> The pit underneath a water-wheel.

Pot-Growan
> Soft decomposed granite.

Prian
> Soft white clay, esteemed a favourable sign when found in a lode.

Pricker
> A thin piece of iron used to make a hole for the fuse or match to fire a blast.

Prill
> A solid piece of virgin metal, or the button from an assay.

Prilling a sample
> Means the clandestine addition of rich mineral to the sample submitted to the assayer, that the miner may have more gain than is right.

Produce
> Fine copper contained in 100 parts of ore.

Prospecting
> Sinking trial holes on, or in search of lodes.

Pulley (Sheave)
> A small wheel movable about an axis and having a groove cut in its circumference, over which a rope passes.

Pulveriser
> A machine for grinding the ores.

Pump
> A cylinder of iron about 9ft, long, used for conducting water up the shaft, a portion of a lift, or line of pumps.

Purser
> The cashier or paymaster at the mine.

(Q)

Quartz
> Sqar, crystalline silica.

Quere (also spelt Queere or Qweear)
> A small cavity or fissure; joint.

(R)

Rack (or Rag Frame)
> An inclined frame on which ores and slimes are washed and separated.

Racking
> A process of separating small ore from the earthy particles by means of an inclined wooden frame; the impurities being washed off, and the ore remaining near the head of the rack taken thence, undergoes tossing.

Ragger

    The man who breaks the large blocks of ore.

Reed, or Spire

    Gorse, or other tubular vegetable, into which gunpowder is put to convey a train from the match to the charge, the reed being put into the aperture made by the needle. This mode of ignition has been superseded by a metalic tube, or fuse.

Refining

    Separating the ores.

Relief

    When one workman of the same pare changes core, or takes the place of another.

Returning charges

    (see standard).

Riddle, or griddle

    A Sieve.

Rising

    Digging upwards. Raise or rise is a steeply inclined excavation.

Rock-Drill

    (see drill).

Row

    Rough large stones.

Royalty

    The lord's portion of the produce; dues, or "dish".

Rubbish

    Deads, Debris, attle.

Pullers

    The persons who works the wheelbarrows underground.

Run

    When excavations collapse; or when through failure of supports, or the loose constitution of the rocks, the stuff falls in a level or shaft.

Run of a lode

    Its direction or strike.

Rush

    Formerly used to convey powder to the blasting charge.

(S)

Safety-Fuse

    A thin train of powder contained in a long cotton envelope, made water proof, inserted in the hole to ignite the explosive. (invented 1830).

Saw Mill
Workshop at surface where sawyers use machines for cutting timber for use in the mine.

Scal, or Scale
A shale or portion of earth, rock, etc., which separates and falls from the main body.

Sampling
The taking of a portion of ore for the assayer.

Schorlaceous
Processing the properties of schorl.

Schorl Rock
A mineral usually occurring in black prismatic crystals. It is brittle and has much lustre, and becomes electric by heat and friction.

Scorran
St. Just term for an irony quartz vein.

Scovan Lode
A lode having no gossan on its back, or near the surface.

Scraper
A piece of iron used to take out the pulverised matter which remains in the hole when bored previous to blasting.

Seam
A horse load.

Serpentine
A rock abundant at the Lizard, generally unstratified, principally composed of hydrated silicate of magnesia. Wrought into ornaments of great variety.

Sett
A lease stating the boundaries and terms of the mining ground taken by the adventurers.

Set of Timber
A frame, complete, to support each side of the vein, level, or shaft.

Set-off
The part of a connecting rod to which the bucket rod is attached.

Shaft
A pit either on the lode or through the "country".

Shaft Pare
Men sinking the shaft.

Shaking

Washing the ores.

Shallow Adit

A drift to drain the mine a few fathoms deep, that the lode may be tried before incurring the cost of a deep adit.

Shammel

When ore or water is lifted part of the required height by one machine or person, and part by another.

Shears

Two very high pieces of wood placed in a vertical position on each side of the shaft, and united at the top, over which, on a pulley, passes the capstan rope; erected for the convenience of lifting out of, or lowering into, the shaft, timber, pipes, or other things of great length and weight.

Shelf

The firm rock nearest the surface.

Sheave

The pulley over which the whim rope passes.

Shoding

Tracing round stones from the vale to the lode, whence they were torn by some convulsion of nature.

Shode

Debris fallen from back of lode.

Shooting

Blasting; fracturing by the use of explosive.

Side Lode

A lode near the main lode.

Sieves

Instruments for cleaning tin.

Sigger

(See Zyghyr).

Sinking

Digging downwards.

Skimpings

Skimmings of the light ore, etc., in the dressing process.

Skip

A large box or frame work, in which the stuff is brought up from the mine by the steam whim; and by which, sometimes, unlawfully, men are raised from, and let down into the mine.

Slickenslide

A rock that has acquired a metallic lustre by friction.

Slide

A vein of clay, intersecting a lode, occasions a vertical dislocation.

Slimes

Mud containing metallic ores; mud or earthy particles mixed with the ore.

Smelting House

The house where the ore is reduced to pure metal by means of fire.

Snoff, or Match

A substance, frequently brown paper, or other slowly combustible substance, which is ignited at one end, the other being in contact with the train in blasting; the slow combustion is to permit the labourers to escape. This is now superseded by the safety-fuse.

Sollar

A small platform at the end of a ladder; also the covering of a shaft.

Spale

A fine imposed on a miner for breach of a rule.

Spaller

A person who spalls. (See spalling).

Spalling

The breaking up into small pieces, for the sake of easily separating the ore from the rock; after which it undergoes the process of cobbing.

Span-Beam

The horizontal beam passing over the whim, in which the upper pivot of the perpendicular axis moves.

Spar

Crystalline white mineral, either quartz, lime, or felspar.

Squat

A "pocket" of ore (see bunch).

Stamps, or Stamping Mill

Machinery for crushing the ores mixed with water (Fig 10 and 11).

Stamps Head

The iron weight, or head, connected with the "lifter" in the stamps, which bruises the ore by its fall. (Fig 10 and 11).

Standard

The price of fine copper.

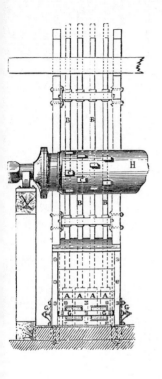

Stamping (Fig's. 10 & 11)

The ore being broken down nearly to the size of road stone, is in a fit state for the action of the "stamps" or "crushers", the former being mostly used for tin ores. The stamps that were in ordinary use in Cornwall are shown in Fig's 10 & 11. The ore is tipped on to the slope, D, Fig. 11, and gradually makes its way down under the heavy stamp heads, A. These, weighing from 4 to 8 cwt. each, are lifted successively by means of their lifters, and the cams, c, on the revolving axle, H, to a height of 10 or 12 inches, and, falling on the ore, speedily reduce it to fine powder. Water is continually supplied from a "launder", as shown in fig. 11, and this facilitates the escape of the fine particles of ore through the gratings or "Stamp grates", GG.

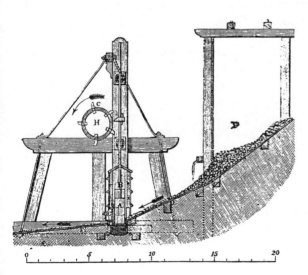

Stannary Laws
    Regulations for the management, etc., of tinners in Devon and
    Cornwall.
Steam Engine
    (see engine). (Fig 2).
Steam Whim
    A whim driven by steam.
Stem
    A day's work.
Stock Work
    Where the veins of ore are very numerous and small. Applies to
    underground and surface. Carclaze is a typical opencast example.
Stope
    A horizontal bed; ore ground adjacent to the levels; to stope,
    to excavate horizontally, layer after layer. Underhand stoping
    is the working below the level, and overhand, working above
    it.
Spend
    To break ground; to work away.
Stent
    The limits within which the miners work during one "taking".
    Also rock waste in china clay mining.
Strake
    A launder or box of wood without ends, in which the process of
    washing or tying is performed.
Strapping plates
    The iron plates by which the pump rods are fastened to each other.
    See Fig 2C & Fig 6.
Strata
    The rocks in which the minerals are found.
Stream Tin
    Tin ore found in the form of pebbles in valleys; common in
    Cornwall.
Stream Works
    Places where detrital tin is washed.
Streamers
    The persons who work in search of stream tin.
Strike of the lode
    Bearing of the lode.

String
    A small vein.
Stroke
    The motion of the pumping engine caused by one injection of the steam.
Stuff
    Attle, or rubbish; debris.
Stull
    Timber placed in the backs of levels, and covered with boards or small poles to support rubbish.
Sturt or Start
    When a tributer takes a pitch at a high tribute, and cuts a course of ore, he sometimes gets £200 to £500 in two months; this great success is called a sturt.
Sump
    A pit; the bottom of the engine shaft.
Sump-shaft
    The engine shaft.
Sumpmen
    Men who assist the pit man, sink the engine shaft and attend to the machinery in the engine shaft.

(T)

Tackle
    Windlass, rope and kibble.
Tacknote
    A licence to search for mineral before a lease is granted.
Tail of Adit
    The place where the adit water leaves the adit at the portal, sometimes called the "mouth" of the adit. (See Fig 5).
Tailings
    Refuse from the last dressing operations.
Take
    A miner's bargain for one or two months.
Tamping
    The material, usually clay, placed on the gunpowder, in order to confine force, which would otherwise pass up the hole; also the process of placing the material.
Tamping Iron, or Bar
    Tool used for beating down the earthy substance on the charge used in blasting.

Team
> To lade water in bowls.

Thrown
> (either up or down). Is when a slide intersects a lode, the dislocation being shown by a traverse section. Thrown up, is when the undiscovered portion of the intersected lode is found to have been apparently lengthened; thrown down is the reverse.

Ticketing
> The sale of ores by tender.

Timberman
> The man employed in placing supports of timber in the interior of the mine. The work is called "timbering".

Tin Bounds
> (See bounds).

Tinner
> A worker on tin.

Tin-Ore
> Black tin ready for the smelter.

Tin Pyrites
> Sulphide of copper and tin; bell metal ore.

Toller
> A person who occasionally examines the workings on behalf of the lord.

Ton
> The ton varies in different districts. The legal ton is 20cwt. of 112 lbs. or 2240 lbs, in Cornwall the mining ton was 21 cwt, of 112 lbs, or 2352 lbs.

Touch-Pipe
> A brief abstention from labour, during which the miner takes his lunch or smokes his pipe.

Tossing, or Tozing
> A process consisting in suspending the ores by violent agitation in water, their subsidence being accelerated by packing, the lighter and worthless matter remains uppermost.

Tourmaline Schist.
> Schorlaceous schist.

Trade
> Attle, rubbish, or very poor ores.

Tram Carriage
> The carriage (usually made of iron) used on a tramroad.

38

Trammers

Persons who conduct the tram carriages.

Trap Door

A door in a level to stop current of air.

Trawn

A cross course, so called in St. Just, only.

Treloobing

(see tossing).

Tribute

Proportion of the ore which the workman has for his labour. (Tributer).

Tributers

Men whose pay is a certain proportion of the ores, or of the value of the ores they raise.

Tribute Pitches

The limited portions of a lode set to "a pare" of tributers; beyond which they are not permitted for the time being to work.

Trommel

An apparatus for the classifying of ores.

Trunk

A long narrow cistern or pit, in which the ore and slimes, which are mixed, are separated by the subsidence of the former, and the washing off the impurities are separated in the process of trunking.

Trunking

Process of extracting ores from the slimes; subsequently the ores undergo the process fo racking and tossing.

Tummals

A great quantity; or heap.

Tunnel Head

The top of a furnace, at which the materials are put in.

Turning House

The first cutting on the lode after it is cut in a cross-cut.

Turned House

A term used when a level, in following branches of ore, is turned from the original direction.

Tutwork

Work in which the labourer earns in proportion to the amount of his labour, being paid for driving, sinking, at a certain price per fathom, or so much for a "job".

Tuyere
  The aperture through which the air or blast is introduced into the furnace.
Tying
  Washing of minerals.
Tye
  A long trough to separate roughs from slimes by washing.

(U)

Umber
  Oxide of iron and of manganese.
Underlie shaft
  A diagonal shaft on the course of the lode.

(V)

Van
  The tin ore washed and cleaned on a shovel.
Vugh, Vugg, or Vogle
  A cavity.

(W)

Wad
  The earthy oxide of manganese.
Washing
  The copper ore at times undergoes 2 or 3 washings; the first process being that of washing the slime and earthy particles from the rougher and large stones of ore.
Water in fork
  When all the water has been extracted.
Water Wheel
  A wheel containing buckets into which water flows, the gravitation of which acts as a lever on the axle, to which are attached arrangements for stamping, grinding, sawing, pumping, etc.

Wedged-Out
    When the walls of the lode come together, it is said to be "wedged
    out".
Well
    The lower part of the furnace into which the metal falls.
Wheal
    A corruption of the word "Huel", which means a hole, or mine
    pit. A prefix to the names of most mines.
Wheel
    See water wheel.
Wheel-Barrow
    A frame with a box, supported by a wheel, and rolled by a single
    man.
Whim
    A machine worked by steam, horse, or water, for raising ores, etc.
Whim Driver
    The man who attends to the horses in the whim, or to the whim
    engine.
Whim Rope or Chain
    The rope or chain by which the kibble is attached to the winding
    engine, or whim.
Whim Shaft
    The shaft through which the stuff is drawn out of the mine by
    horse or steam whim.
Whip and Derry
    A kibble drawn to the surface by a horse, the rope attaching one to
    the other, and simply passing over a pulley. This mode of drawing
    the stuff is called "whip and derry".
White Iron
    Spathose Iron.
Wild-Lead
    Blende, zinc ore.
Winch
    Contraction of "windlass"; the wheel and axle used for drawing
    water, etc. in a kibble by a rope; also a machine for lifting heavy
    bodies.
Windbore
    The lowest pump in each lift in a shaft, in which there are holes to
    admit water to be pumped by the engine to the next cistern.
Winding Engine
    One used to draw up ore, attle, etc from the mine.

Windlass
(See winch).
Winze
A sink on the lode communicating one level with the other, for proving the lode, or for ventilation.
Wire Rope
The modern rope used in mines instead of chains and hempen rope of even older times. (First used S. Frances 1860 (Germany, 1830's)).
Wits
The undressed tin nearest the stamps after reduction, being the "crop" of the stuff.
Work
Ores are drawn up, before they are cleansed or dressed.
Working Barrel
The pump in which the piston works.
Working big
When a drift is sufficiently large for a man to work in conveniently.

(Z)

Zyghyr
When a slow small stream of water issues through a cranny it is said to zyghyr or sigger.